W9-AYA-462

MARVEL

"TSUM TSUM"

TAKEOVER!

MARVEL TSUM TSUM: TAKEOVER! (SCHOLASTIC EDITION). Contains material originally published in magazine form as MARVEL TSUM TSUM #1-4. First printing 2016. ISBN# 978-1-302-90722-8. Published by MARVEL WORLDWIDE, INC., a subsidiary of MARVEL ENTERTAINMENT, LLC. OFFICE OF PUBLICATION: 135 West 50th Street, New York, NY 10020. Copyright © 2016 MARVEL No similarity between any of the names, characters, persons, and/or institutions in this magazine with those of any living or dead person or institution is intended, and any such similarity which may exist is purely coincidental. **Printed in the U.S.A.** ALAN FINE, President, Marvel Entertainment; DAN BUCKLEY, President, TV, Publishing & Brand Management; JOE QUESADA, Chief Creative Officer; TOM BREVOORT, SVP of Publishing; DAVID BOGART, SVP of Business Affairs & Operations, Publishing & Partnership; C.B. CEBULSKI, VP of Brand Management & Development, Asia; DAVID GABRIEL, SVP of Sales & Marketing, Publishing; JEFF YOUNGQUIST, VP of Production & Special Projects; DAN CARR, Executive Director of Publishing Technology; ALEX MORALES, Director of Publishing Operations; SUSAN CRESPI, Production Manager; STAN LEE, Chairman Emeritus. For information regarding advertising in Marvel Comics or on Marvel.com, please contact Vit DeBellis, Integrated Sales Manager, at vdebellis@marvel. com. For Marvel subscription inquiries, please call 888-511-5480. **Manufactured between 10/28/2016 and 12/5/2016 by COMMAND WEB MISSOURI, JEFFERSON CITY, MO, USA.**

10 9 8 7 6 5 4 3 2 1

COLLECTION EDITOR: **JENNIFER GRÜNWALD** • ASSOCIATE MANAGING EDITOR: **KATERI WOODY**
ASSOCIATE EDITOR: **SARAH BRUNSTAD** • EDITOR, SPECIAL PROJECTS: **MARK D. BEAZLEY**
VP PRODUCTION & SPECIAL PROJECTS: **JEFF YOUNGQUIST**
SVP PRINT, SALES & MARKETING: **DAVID GABRIEL** • COVER DESIGN: **ADAM DEL RE**

EDITOR IN CHIEF: **AXEL ALONSO** • CHIEF CREATIVE OFFICER: **JOE QUESADA**
PUBLISHER: **DAN BUCKLEY** • EXECUTIVE PRODUCER: **ALAN FINE**

MARVEL
"TSUM TSUM

TAKEOVER!

WRITER: **JACOB CHABOT**

PENCILER: **DAVID BALDEON**

INKERS: **TERRY PALLOT**

WITH **SCOTT HANNA** (#3)

COLORIST: **JIM CAMPBELL**

LETTERERS: **VC'S TRAVIS LANHAM** (#1)

& **CORY PETIT** (#2-4)

COVER ART: **CHRIS SAMNEE** & **MATTHEW WILSON**

ASSISTANT EDITOR: **ALLISON STOCK**

EDITOR: **DEVIN LEWIS**

EXECUTIVE EDITORS: **NICK LOWE** & **C.B. CEBULSKI**

SPECIAL THANKS TO **SCOTT DOLPH** & **SATOSHI KUBO**

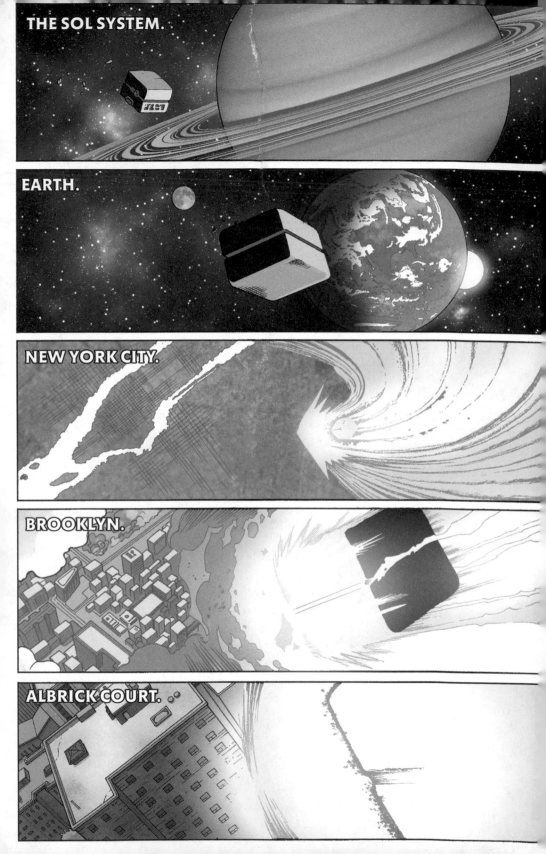

THE SOL SYSTEM.

EARTH.

NEW YORK CITY.

BROOKLYN.

ALBRICK COURT.

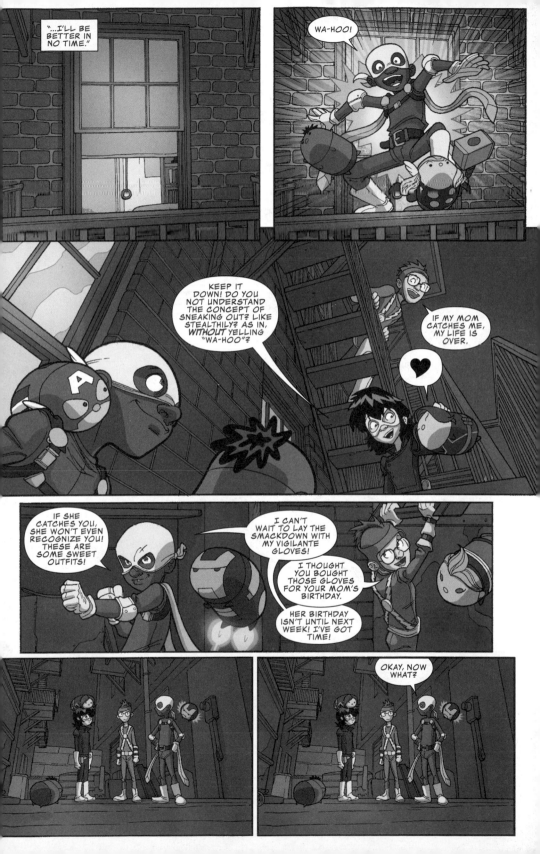

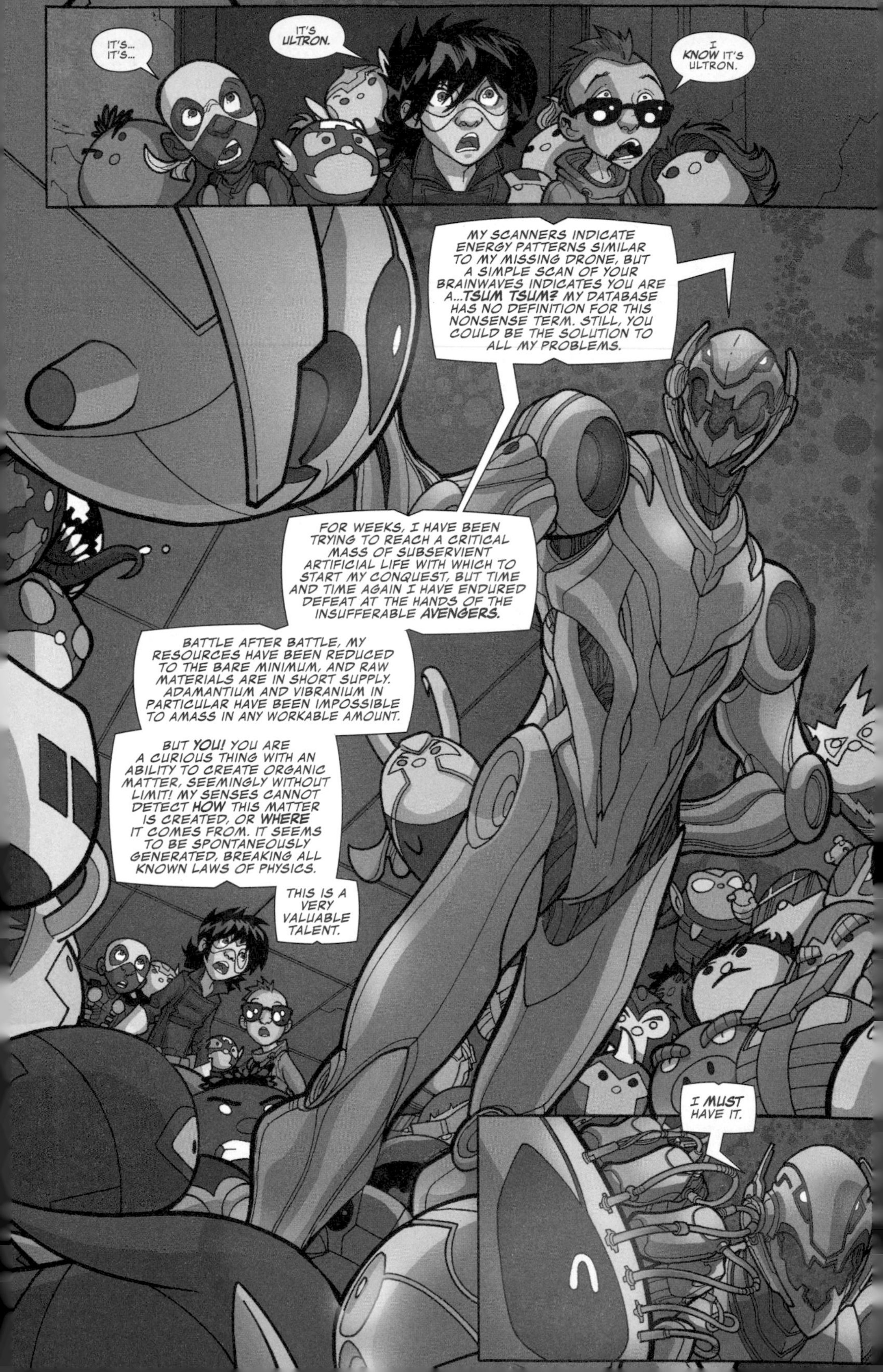
IT'S... IT'S...
IT'S ULTRON.
I KNOW IT'S ULTRON.
MY SCANNERS INDICATE ENERGY PATTERNS SIMILAR TO MY MISSING DRONE, BUT A SIMPLE SCAN OF YOUR BRAINWAVES INDICATES YOU ARE A...TSUM TSUM? MY DATABASE HAS NO DEFINITION FOR THIS NONSENSE TERM. STILL, YOU COULD BE THE SOLUTION TO ALL MY PROBLEMS.
FOR WEEKS, I HAVE BEEN TRYING TO REACH A CRITICAL MASS OF SUBSERVIENT ARTIFICIAL LIFE WITH WHICH TO START MY CONQUEST, BUT TIME AND TIME AGAIN I HAVE ENDURED DEFEAT AT THE HANDS OF THE INSUFFERABLE AVENGERS.
BATTLE AFTER BATTLE, MY RESOURCES HAVE BEEN REDUCED TO THE BARE MINIMUM, AND RAW MATERIALS ARE IN SHORT SUPPLY. ADAMANTIUM AND VIBRANIUM IN PARTICULAR HAVE BEEN IMPOSSIBLE TO AMASS IN ANY WORKABLE AMOUNT.
BUT YOU! YOU ARE A CURIOUS THING WITH AN ABILITY TO CREATE ORGANIC MATTER, SEEMINGLY WITHOUT LIMIT! MY SENSES CANNOT DETECT HOW THIS MATTER IS CREATED, OR WHERE IT COMES FROM. IT SEEMS TO BE SPONTANEOUSLY GENERATED, BREAKING ALL KNOWN LAWS OF PHYSICS.
THIS IS A VERY VALUABLE TALENT.
I MUST HAVE IT.

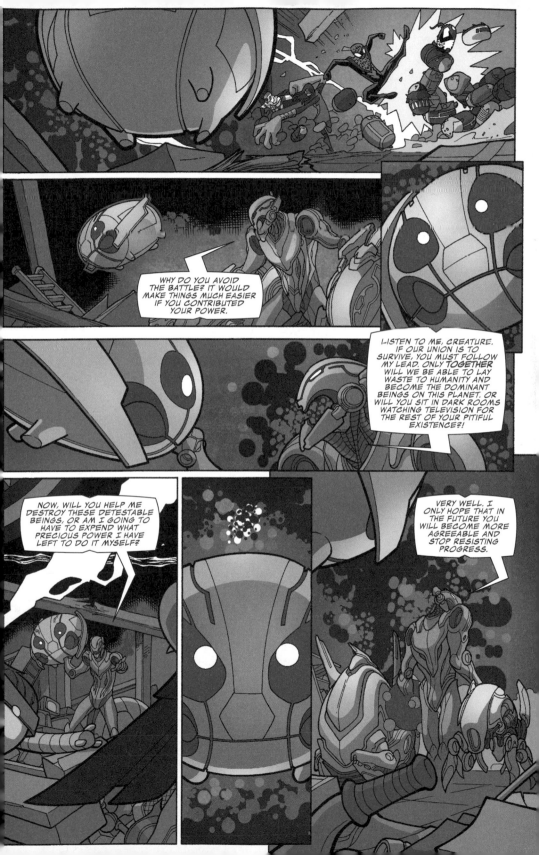

IT'S TIME TO GET OUT OF THIS LOUSY TOWN AND PUT ALL THIS MADNESS IN MY REARVIEW. I'VE GOT ENOUGH HERE TO SET ME UP SOMEPLACE NICE. SOMEPLACE FAAAAR AWAY.

BARBADOS IS PROBABLY NICE THIS TIME OF YEAR.

RIIIIIING

YEAH? OH, HEY, MR. HAMMERHEAD!

YES, THAT WAS ME ON THE MIDTOWN JOB. THANKS FOR THE KIND WORDS! NO, SORRY. TRADE SECRET. I CAN'T TELL YOU HOW I PULLED IT OFF.

ACTUALLY, MR. H, THAT OFFER IS REAL FLATTERING, BUT I WAS JUST ABOUT TO GET OUT OF

WHAT WAS THAT? NORTON? NORTON, ARE YOU THERE?

I'M GOING TO HAVE TO CALL YOU BACK.

EPILOGUE.
THE COLLECTOR'S BASE OF OPERATIONS.

AT LAST! THE TSUM TSUM ARE IN MY POSSESSION!

I'VE BEEN WAITING FOR EONS TO ADD THESE RARE BEINGS TO MY COLLECTION!

!

?!

WAUGH!

THE END!

MARVEL TSUM TSUM 1 VARIANT
BY FERNANDO OLMEDO, DISNEY INTERACTIVE & MARVEL

MARVEL TSUM TSUM 2 VARIANT
BY FERNANDO OLMEDO, DISNEY INTERACTIVE & MARVEL

MARVEL TSUM TSUM 3 VARIANT
BY FERNANDO OLMEDO, DISNEY INTERACTIVE & MARVEL

MARVEL TSUM TSUM 4 VARIANT
BY FERNANDO OLMEDO, DISNEY INTERACTIVE & MARVEL

MARVEL TSUM TSUM 1 VARIANT
BY TERRY DODSON & RACHEL DODSON

**MARVEL TSUM TSUM 1 VARIANT
BY JAMAL CAMPBELL**

**MARVEL TSUM TSUM 1 VARIANT
BY SUJIN LEE**

**MARVEL TSUM TSUM 1 VARIANT
BY ALEX KROPINAK**

**MARVEL TSUM TSUM 1 VARIANT
BY GURIHIRU**

MARVEL TSUM TSUM 2 VARIANT
BY GUSTAVO DUARTE

**MARVEL TSUM TSUM 3 VARIANT
BY CORY SMITH & ANDRES MOSSA**

**MARVEL TSUM TSUM 4 VARIANT
BY DAVE JOHNSON**

**AMAZING SPIDER-MAN VARIANT
BY CHRIS SAMNEE & MATTHEW WILSON**

**ALL-NEW, ALL-DIFFERENT AVENGERS VARIANT
BY KRIS ANKA**

**ALL-NEW WOLVERINE VARIANT
BY JACOB PARKER**

**UNCANNY INHUMANS VARIANT
BY GUISEPPE CAMUNCOLI & JASON KEITH**

BLACK PANTHER VARIANT
BY SARA PICHELLI & JASON KEITH

DEADPOOL VARIANT
BY JAVIER RODRIGUEZ & ALVARO LOPEX

MS. MARVEL VARIANT
BY TRADD MOORE & MATTHEW WILSON

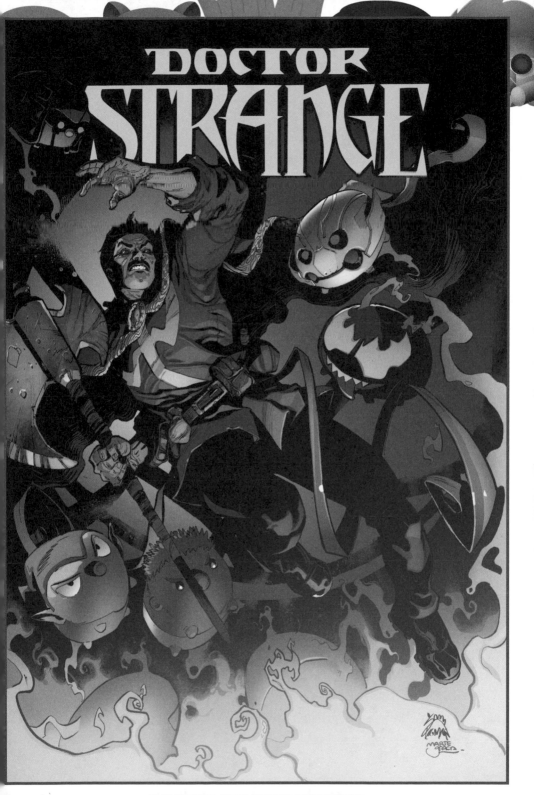

DOCTOR STRANGE VARIANT
BY RYAN STEGMAN & MARTE GRACIA

**MIGHTY THOR VARIANT
BY NATACHA BUSTOS**

**GUARDIANS OF THE GALAXY VARIANT
BY RON LIM & RACHELLE ROSENBERG**

ROCKET RACCOON & GROOT VARIANT
BY BRIAN KENSINGER

**INVINCIBLE IRON MAN VARIANT
BY BRANDON PETERSON**

MOON GIRL & DEVIL DINOSAUR VARIANT
BY JOËLLE JONES & RACHELLE ROSENBERG